Dairy Free Cooking

Dairy Free Cooking – healthy eating following cancer

Copyright © 2009 Evans Mitchell Books

Text: Copyright © 2009 Lois Whittaker

Food design & photography by: Shootingfood, www.shootingfood.co.uk
Stock imagery from Dreamstime and iStock

Lois Whittaker has asserted her rights to be identified as the author
and photographer of this work in accordance with Section 77 of the
Copyright, Designs and Patents Act 1988.

First published in the United Kingdom in 2009 by:
Evans Mitchell Books
The Old Forge, Forge Mews
16 Church Street
Rickmansworth
Hertfordshire WD3 1DH
United Kingdom
www.embooks.co.uk

Design by: Darren Westlake, TU ink Ltd, London. www.tuink.co.uk

Edited by: Elaine Koster

British Library Cataloguing in Publication Data. A CIP record of this
book is available on request from the British Library.

ISBN: 978-1-901268-49-2

Printed in China

Evans Mitchell Books

Dairy Free Cooking

TIPS ON
Healthy eating
following cancer

LOIS WHITTAKER

Contents

every day dairy-free cooking

KEY TO SYMBOLS

The three symbols above accompany every recipe and represent (from left to right):

1   Servings, ie. '4 people'

2   Preparation time

3   Cooking time

CHAPTERS

Whether it's brunch, lunch or dining out, take a fresh look at food. Don't go without – go free. Dairy free!

Introduction

Two years ago I finished a gruelling round of operations and chemotherapy for breast cancer. Much of the literature on diet suggested that dairy free was the best option for my type of cancer (oestrogen-based breast cancer) and I was encouraged to give up dairy completely, even after my treatment had finished, as a precaution to try and prevent any return of my cancer.

But how do you change your diet? Where do you start?

I thought I had a fairly healthy diet, but when I started to analyse what I eat it was very dairy heavy. My staple food was cereal with milk for breakfast, cheese sandwiches for lunch or a jacket potato with tuna and cheese, and for supper pasta with cheese, such as spaghetti carbonara, cauliflower cheese or lasagne (more cheese!).

I spoke to lots of ladies at the oncology clinic who were struggling with how to change their diet. So I decided to write this book.

In addition, many people these days seem to have an allergy to dairy products so I wanted to share what I had learnt over the last few years.

This is not just a bunch of recipes – it is intended for people struggling with having to change their diet and lifestyle as a result of a debilitating illness. If this book helps just one person cope a little better with dealing with cancer, then it will have been worth writing.

This is me on holiday in Dubai visiting my niece, Verity. As you can see I have lots of hair! Yes, it does grow back after the chemo and mine grew back even thicker and curlier than ever!

Thank goodness for hair straighteners!

Useful tips

Treats
My best find was Lindt 70% dark chocolate. Many dark chocolates are quite bitter – I should know as I have tried them all! But this one is so creamy that it just melts in your mouth. It is fab and certainly stopped me from craving for sweet things. I always keep a few bars in the cupboard. Personally I think it tastes better when it is not kept in the fridge, but that's just me! Lindt is available from most large supermarkets – Tesco, Waitrose and Sainsburys all stock it.

Not all dark chocolate is dairy free, so check the label before you buy it. My favourite treat was Green and Black's Maya Gold but they changed their recipe in 2008 and now it contains milk.

Cereals
I love cereals but eating them without milk is a problem. So I use fruit juice. Grapefruit juice is great as it is not too sweet. Orange juice also works, depending on the cereal. You get a few odd looks at the breakfast table when you tip your orange juice onto your cornflakes! But it tastes fine.

Sandwiches
Pure is a dairy-free spread. Again it is available from most large supermarkets and tastes really nice.

If you fancy a sandwich but have no dairy-free spread, use olive oil, salad cream or mayonnaise. Both taste fine and are a good substitute for dairy.

Again check the label as many spreads contain buttermilk, or some dairy.

Look out for these other tips throughout the book!

TIP

If a food label stipulates it is okay for **vegans**, then it is dairy free, so you can add it to your list of foods.

Useful tips

Soya Products

Be careful about substituting soya milk or soya-based products for dairy. Many health books have concerns about soya depending on your type of cancer. So my suggestion is stick to black coffee, black tea, green tea and herbal teas, or hot water with a few slices of lemon. But if you are going through treatment for cancer, check with your oncologist first before changing your diet.

My oncologist said I could have camel's milk, but I haven't yet found anywhere that sells it! I guess I could catch my own camel and give it a go!

Labels

Always read the label – watch out as some breads contain milk and even things you thought should be okay often contain milk.

When you are going through chemo everything has a metallic taste so it is really hard to eat properly. But this is just the time when you must get those fruit and vegetables inside you.

You will find that many of my recipes use both fruit and vegetables, partly because they taste good together, but also as a way of increasing your fruit and veg intake without really realising it!

These recipes are not complicated or time consuming. But they are healthy and nutritious! So enjoy...

And if the rest of your family cannot bear the thought of no dairy, then there are also suggestions for how to cater for both dairy and non-dairy eaters with the minimum of fuss.

TIP

Cure those cravings!

- If you need something more **savoury**, marmite makes a great hot drink – but I guess you either love it or you hate it!

- If you want a **sweeter drink**, I like cranberry and apple juice with hot water.

- **Raisins and grapes** are also good if you are craving for something sweet. I usually buy those tiny packets of raisins and mix them with a few green seedless grapes.

What to keep
in the store cupboard

CONVERSIONS

Metric	Imperial
15 ml	½ fl oz
60 ml	2 fl oz
125 ml	4 ½ fl oz
200 ml	7 fl oz
250 ml	9 fl oz
100 g	3 ½ oz
250 g	9 oz
500 g	1 lb 2 oz
1 kg	2 ¼ lb

Balsamic vinegar – for salad dressings and cooking.

Extra virgin olive oil – for frying, grilling and marinating.

Ground nut oil or sunflower oil – these don't have a strong taste so can be used for frying, grilling, etc.

Coconut milk – this is a good alternative for milk and is used in many Thai recipes.

Borlotti beans – these are a staple bean and can be used to bulk up any dish. They also taste delicious in pastas, stews and soups.

Butter beans – great on their own as a vegetable or in stews.

Chickpeas – for making hummus and many Moroccan dishes.

Basmati rice – nicer than brown wholemeal rice, but still good for you.

Arborio rice – for risotto.

Pasta – ideally wholemeal pasta.

Tinned tomatoes – many dishes use tomatoes.

Jar of sun-dried tomatoes – to give a more intense flavour.

Tomato purée – you can also buy the sun-dried tomato purée which is great for a change.

Jars of herbs – bouquet garni, cinnamon, mixed herbs – keep these in the cupboard for when you need those extra spices to add to a recipe.

Stock cubes – great for gravy, soups, casseroles, etc.

Bottle of dry martini – as it contains herbs adding a capful to sauces, for pasta dishes etc., gives them a bit of oomph!

Dark chocolate – everyone needs treats!

Caster sugar – for baking.

Raisins or sultanas – for Thai dishes and baking or just if you need a sweet snack.

TIP

It really is worth investing in a food processor. Soups, dips, pâtés, etc., are all so easy with a food processor, and it will save you hours in the kitchen.

Real comfort food
rustic soups

INSIDE THIS SECTION

TIP

Whenever I make a soup I always make enough for a few days and freeze it. Then you have a quick and tasty meal ready for another day.

Making soup

- **quick and tasty**
- **full of vitamins**
- **stores for a week**
- **can freeze and keep**

INGREDIENTS

A little olive oil

1 red onion (100g), peeled and diced

1 potato (100g), peeled and chopped
into small chunks

300g chopped vegetables of your
choice, or a mixture

1 litre chicken or vegetable stock

Salt and pepper to taste

METHOD

Soup is a great way of getting loads of vitamins, whilst at the same time using up all the vegetables left over in the fridge. And it is very easy to make! This basic recipe can be used for any soups. Just adapt depending on what vegetables you have available.

1   In a saucepan heat the olive oil, then add the chopped onion and cook gently for 3-5 minutes, until soft but not coloured.

2   Then add the potatoes and turn them well until coated with oil. Cover and sweat on a gentle heat for 10 minutes.

3   Add the vegetables and stock and simmer for 20 minutes or until the vegetables are soft. Season to taste.

4   Either serve as is, or cool and whizz in a blender for a smoother soup.

5   Return soup to pan, heat and serve with warm crusty bread.

TIPS

- If you are not good at measuring just remember **1, 1, 3.** So, 1 part onion, 1 part potato, 3 parts vegetable.

- If you prefer a **thicker soup,** add less stock.

- If you prefer a **thinner soup,** add less potato, or even no potato. Just experiment until you get the thickness and consistency you like.

- I prefer to use **red onions** as they have a slightly milder taste and don't make me cry when I peel them!

Roasted tomato
and basil soup

 4 people

 10 minutes

 25 minutes

INGREDIENTS

A little olive oil

24 small cherry tomatoes

500ml vegetable stock

1 teaspoon sugar

Handful of basil

Pepper to taste

Parsley to garnish (optional)

METHOD

1 Preheat the oven to 180°C for a fan oven.

2 Roast the tomatoes in the oven with a little olive oil for around 15 minutes until soft.

3 Transfer to a saucepan, add the vegetable stock and a teaspoon of sugar. Cover the pan, bring back to the boil and then reduce the heat and simmer for 10 minutes.

4 Turn off the heat and add the basil. Cool, then whizz in a blender and season to taste.

4 Add a sprig of parsley to garnish and serve.

TIP

Roasting the tomatoes brings out the flavour, but you can also just sweat the tomatoes in a saucepan first and then add the vegetable stock if you prefer, or are short of time.

Ciara and James gave me all the cuddles I needed when I was going through chemo

...and also lent me their favourite toys so I wouldn't be scared in the night!

Butternut squash soup

4 people

10 minutes

30 minutes

This soup is very warming and ideal for a cold winter's day

INGREDIENTS

A little olive oil

1 medium (500g) butternut squash, peeled, seeded and diced

1 granny smith apple, peeled and chopped

A small piece of fresh ginger – around 2cm x 1cm roughly sliced

A pinch of salt

1 teaspoon sugar

600ml vegetable stock

Juice of one medium-sized orange

Pepper to taste

METHOD

1 In a saucepan heat the olive oil, then add the chopped butternut squash, apple, ginger, salt and sugar. Cover and cook on a low heat for 20 minutes, stirring occasionally to prevent sticking, until the squash is very tender.

2 Add the vegetable stock and orange juice. Cover the pan, bring back to the boil and then reduce the heat and simmer for 10 minutes.

3 Cool, then whizz in a blender and season to taste.

4 Return soup to pan, heat and serve with warm crusty bread, ciabbati or bread rolls.

SUGGESTION

Butternut squash is difficult to peel as it is so hard. If you have time, as an alternative you can roast the butternut squash first. Pierce the skin with a knife making a few slits and then place in a preheated oven at 180°C for around 20 minutes. Allow to cool slightly and the skin will just come off in your hands. Then chop the butternut, remove the seeds and add to the recipe. It will now need only about 10 minutes cooking time, as the butternut will be virtually cooked.

TIP

• This soup improves with keeping. Prepare a day in advance and keep refrigerated.

• If you don't like your soup too thick then just add a little more stock.

• Ginger – if it is very wrinkly then it is old and will be hot. So adjust how much you put in the soup, depending on the freshness of the ginger.

Watercress soup

Watercress is a rich source of essential nutrients including calcium, magnesium, phosphorous, potassium, vitamin C and beta-carotene. So it not only tastes delicious, but it is really good for you too.

INGREDIENTS

A little olive oil

1 medium red onion (75g), finely chopped

1 small potato (75g), peeled and chopped

3 x 75g packs watercress, washed (keep a sprig for the garnish)

600ml vegetable stock

Salt and pepper to taste

METHOD

1 Heat the olive oil in a saucepan and cook the onion gently for about 3-5 minutes until soft but not coloured.

2 Add the potato and watercress (leave some for garnish) and turn them well until coated with the olive oil. Cover and sweat on a gentle heat for about 3 minutes.

3 Add the stock and bring back to the boil. Then simmer for about 20 minutes, or until the potatoes are very soft, keeping the cover on the pan.

4 Allow the soup to cool and then whizz in a blender until smooth. Season to taste.

5 Return the soup to the pan and heat through. Before serving garnish with watercress.

Broccoli and courgette soup

4 people

10 minutes

30 minutes

Broccoli is a real nutritional powerhouse. It contains vitamin C, folic acid, potassium, 13C and a chemical called genistein. Research suggests that these chemicals can boost DNA repair in cells and may stop them becoming cancerous.

INGREDIENTS

A little olive oil

1 clove garlic, finely chopped

1 large red onion (100g), finely chopped

200g small broccoli florets

100g courgettes, chopped

600ml vegetable stock

Salt and pepper to taste

METHOD

1   Heat the olive oil in a saucepan and cook the onion and garlic gently for about 3-5 minutes, until soft but not coloured.

2   Add the broccoli and courgettes and cover and sweat the vegetables for about 3 minutes.

3   Pour on the stock and bring to the boil.

4   Cover the pan again and simmer for about 20 minutes, or until the vegetables are very soft.

5   Allow the soup to cool and then whizz in a blender until smooth. Season to taste. Return soup to pan and heat through before serving.

I ate broccoli soup every day for six months when I was going through chemo because I knew how good it was for me. I used to add the courgettes to give it a slightly different taste, just for a change, but you can make the soup just with broccoli and add a potato for a thicker soup.

TIP
You can drizzle the soup with cream before serving for your dairy lovers.

Minestrone soup

 6 people   **10** minutes   **35-40** minutes

INGREDIENTS

A little olive oil

2 medium red onions (75g each), finely chopped

4 large carrots, peeled and sliced

4 stalks celery, thinly sliced

1 clove garlic, chopped

1 medium potato (75g), peeled and diced

100g shredded cabbage

100g petit pois, fresh or frozen

1 400g tin of chopped tomatoes

1 litre vegetable stock

1 tablespoon parsley, chopped

Salt and pepper to taste

METHOD

1 Heat the oil in a saucepan and cook the onion gently for about 3-5 minutes until soft but not coloured.

2 Add the carrot and celery and sweat for 3 minutes.

3 Add the rest of the ingredients and simmer gently for 30 minutes, or until the vegetables are soft, keeping the cover on the pan.

4 Serve steaming hot with crusty bread.

TIP

• This soup improves with keeping. Prepare the day before and keep refrigerated

• If you prefer a smooth soup, then cool and whizz in the blender until smooth. Return the soup to the pan and heat through before serving.

Ham and bean soup

4 people

5-10 minutes

45 minutes

INGREDIENTS

A little olive oil

2 medium red onions,
   (75g each) sliced

1 garlic clove, chopped

1 400g tin plum tomatoes

1 dessertspoon tomato paste

1 litre vegetable stock

240g cooked ham, chopped
   into small squares

1 400g tin borlotti beans,
   drained and rinsed

METHOD

1 Heat the olive oil in a large pan, add the onions and garlic and cook for around 5 minutes on a low heat.

2 Add the tomatoes, tomato paste, stock and cooked ham and bring back to the boil.

3 Cover the pan and gently simmer for around 30 minutes.

4 Allow to cool and then whizz in a blender a small batch at a time and blend until smooth. Return to the pan and bring back to the boil. Add the borlotti beans and simmer for around 10 minutes, then season to taste.

5 Serve with Italian foccacio bread or warm crusty bread. This is a very filling soup!

This is great comfort food – curl up in front of the TV, switch on 'X Factor' and enjoy!

TIP

• Don't add the borlotti beans until the end otherwise they will disappear when liquidised!

Lentil soup

 4 people

 10 minutes

 50 minutes

INGREDIENTS

A little olive oil

2 medium red onions,
    (75g each) finely chopped

150g red split lentils

1 litre vegetable stock

250g passata or 400g tinned
    tomatoes

1 dessertspoon tomato purée

1 bouquet garni

Salt and pepper to taste

METHOD

1   Heat the oil in a saucepan and cook the onion gently for
    about 3-5 minutes until soft but not coloured.

2   Rinse the lentils in cold water and drain. Add to the soup
    with the rest of the ingredients and bring to the boil. Then
    reduce the heat and simmer gently for about 45 minutes,
    or until the vegetables are soft, keeping the cover on the
    pan. Stir occasionally to prevent sticking and add more
    water if required.

3   This soup can be eaten as cooked, or cool. Whizz then
    season the soup in a blender to taste.

4   Serve steaming hot with crusty bread.

TIP

• If you don't want to whizz the soup in the blender, use passata instead of tinned tomatoes. This will give a smooth consistency to the soup.

• Any left-over soup can be reheated and simmered gently until the excess liquid has evaporated and you are left with a smooth purée type consistency. This can then be served as a vegetable bake. Lentils are cheap, nutritious and really good for you.

Quick and easy star

dips, snacks and light bites

...ers

INSIDE THIS SECTION

TIP

• For a great and easy buffet lunch, just make a selection of the dips and pâté and serve with some cold meats and pitta bread or crusty bread. Delicious!

Hummus

4 people

5-10 minutes

0 minutes

Hummus, with its rich earthy taste, is a great dip – an ideal starter served with warmed pitta bread.

INGREDIENTS

150g of tinned or cooked chickpeas

Freshly squeezed juice of 2-3 lemons, or to taste

2 garlic cloves, crushed

Salt, according to taste

A little water

150ml tahina paste

METHOD

1   Drain the chickpeas and keep a few whole ones aside to garnish the dish.

2   Whizz the chickpeas in your blender with the lemon juice and all the other ingredients. Add a little water to ensure the paste is not too thick. Blend to a soft, creamy paste.

3   Put into a serving dish and sprinkle with a few cooked chickpeas.

TIP

• You can buy tahina paste from health food shops and delicatessens. It is made from roasted, pulped sesame seeds and is used extensively in the Middle East in dishes such as hummus and mezze.

• Keep some hummus for the next day and put it in your sandwiches instead of using your dairy-free spread. Or take it as a dip with some raw carrots or celery.

If you want to ring the changes you can add 4 or 5 chopped sun-dried tomatoes into the hummus and then blend. This makes a great tasting hummus. Or add more lemon juice for a more lemony-flavoured hummus. Just experiment with what you like!

Guacamole

4 people   **5-10** minutes   **0** minutes

INGREDIENTS

2 ripe avocados

Juice of 1 lime

Dash of tabasco sauce

Black pepper to season

METHOD

1   Peel and stone the avocados

2   Put the avocado halves into a large bowl and mash roughly with a fork.

3   Add the remaining ingredients and mix well. Season to taste.

4   Serve with tortilla chips or pitta bread.

OR THE REALLY EASY OPTION

Just put all the ingredients into your blender and whizz until a smooth paste!

HOW TO SELECT AND STORE

A ripe, ready to eat avocado should be slightly soft but with no dark, sunken spots or cracks. A firm avocado will ripen in a paper bag or in a fruit basket at room temperature within a few days. As the fruit ripens the skin will turn darker. Avocados should not be refrigerated until they are ripe. Once ripe they can be kept refrigerated for up to a week. But keep them whole and with the skin on to avoid browning, which occurs when the flesh is exposed to air.

TIP

- Avocado contains oleic acid, a monounsaturated fat that may help to lower cholesterol.

- In addition avocados are a good source of potassium, a mineral that helps regulate blood pressure.

Smoked trout pâté

4 people | 5 minutes | 0 minutes

This is so easy to do and tastes delicious.
The only part that takes any time is the washing up!

INGREDIENTS

2 smoked cooked trout fillets,
approx 125g total weight

20-30ml olive oil – enough to
produce a smooth paste

Quarter of a teaspoon of cayenne
pepper or black pepper to taste

1 lemon or 2 limes

METHOD

1 Check for and remove any small bones and then cut the fish into small chunks.

2 Put all ingredients into the blender and whizz until it's a smooth paste. Add more olive oil if you want a smoother pâté.

3 Serve with warm bread or pitta bread cut into triangles.

This can also be done with smoked mackerel.
Take 2 smoked cooked mackerel – remove the skin,
check for any bones and then follow
the recipe as above. For a spicier taste,
add 1 dessertspoon of horseradish sauce.

TIP

 • If I want a starter that I can prepare beforehand, I often make this fish pâté, guacamole and the hummus (pages 24 & 25), and then serve with black olives and warm pitta bread. It works really well.

Visiting the local fish market in
Dubrovnick – couldn't get much fresher!

Olives and coriander

4 people

5-10 minutes

0 minutes

plus **4-5** hours standing time

My brother lives in Cyprus and this is his recipe and hints. Here we have suggested green olives, but use black olives if you prefer a stronger taste.

INGREDIENTS

24 black/green olives

Olive oil

A handful of coriander seeds

Juice of 2 lemons

METHOD

1   Prepare at least 4-5 hours beforehand if possible, to allow the flavours to mix.

2   Take the whole olives and place in a bowl. Add plenty of olive oil. Crush a generous portion of coriander seeds and add to the olives.

3   Squeeze the juice of 2 lemons, and pour over the olives and stir gently until mixed through.

4   Chill in the fridge, stirring once or twice, for the best taste.

✳ Although olives can be enjoyed all year round, in Cyprus they particularly look forward to savouring the first of the crop. The green olives are gathered by hand and then painstakingly cracked with a stone, one by one and then soaked in water, changed every day for 10 to 14 days. The olives are packed in jars of brine for between 2 and 4 weeks and then are ready for eating. They are packed with flavour!

This is me with my 'Big Bro' in Cyprus. He's pretending to be Harrison Ford!

My brother's wonderful olives – bursting with Cypriot flavour!

TIP
• For a fab taste add fresh coriander, finely chopped, instead of coriander seeds.

Tapenade (olive paste)

4 people · **5 minutes** · **0 minutes**

INGREDIENTS

150g tin pitted black olives, drained

100g jar or tin anchovies in oil

30ml capers, drained

A little olive oil (about a tablespoonful)

Freshly-squeezed juice of 1 lemon (30ml)

Black pepper to taste

METHOD

1 Place the olives, anchovies (with their oil) and the capers in a food processor. Add the olive oil and lemon juice while the machine is running until the mixture resembles a rough-textured paste.

2 Add pepper to taste.

3 Serve spread on toasted bread brushed with olive oil.

TIP

• Go easy on the capers as they have a strong flavour!

Melon and avocado salad

4 people | 10 minutes | 0 minutes

INGREDIENTS

1 galia melon

2 avocados, sliced

Juice of 1 freshly-squeezed lemon

20 cherry tomatoes

120g bag of watercress, rocket
and spinach

METHOD

1 Add the salad leaves to a serving/salad bowl.

2 If you have a melon baller, make around 20 melon balls
from the melon. If not, cut into chunks and add to the salad.

3 Slice each avocado into eight pieces, and add to the salad.
Squeeze the lemon juice over the avocados to prevent
them from going brown.

4 Cut the cherry tomatoes in half and add to the salad.

TIP

• This is a quick lunch served
with some smoked salmon
or gravadlax.

• I find that the juice from the
lemon is sufficient for the salad
not to require any dressing,
and of course that's also a
very healthy option!

Mango and prawns

4 people

5-10 minutes

0 minutes

This tastes delicious, looks great and takes no time at all to prepare.

INGREDIENTS

32-40 cooked tiger prawns
    (allow 8-10 per person)

2 ripe mangos

A few fresh coriander leaves

Squeeze of a fresh lime

METHOD

1   Take a wine glass or something similar, as this dish looks much sexier when served in a glass.

2   Peel the mango and cut into small chunks.

3   Arrange layers of prawns and mango in individual glasses.

4   Add a few coriander leaves for decoration and serve.

TIP

• This is so easy. I call it my stress free starter. But do check that your guests like prawns, as not everyone is a fan of shellfish!

Warm **spinach, bacon**
and cherry tomato salad

4 people | **5-10** minutes | **5-10** minutes

INGREDIENTS

120g bag of spinach, rocket and
watercress leaves

20 small cherry tomatoes

1 ripe avocado

Juice of 1 lemon

4 medium sized mushrooms, sliced

4-6 slices of smoked back bacon,
cut into strips

A little olive oil

2 tablespoons balsamic vinegar

Handful of flaked almonds
(optional)

METHOD

1 Wash the salad leaves and arrange them in a large bowl. Cut the cherry tomatoes in half and cut the avocado into quarters or chunks, whatever you prefer, then add to the salad. Drizzle a little lemon juice on the avocado to prevent it from browning.

2 Slice the mushrooms finely and fry with the bacon in olive oil until the mushrooms are cooked and the bacon is nice and crisp. Turn off the heat, add the balsamic vinegar to the pan and leave it until it is warmed through.

3 Dress the salad with the bacon, mushrooms and yummy balsamic vinegar dressing.

4 If you have time, fry the flaked almonds in a little olive oil and then add to the salad.

5 Eat straight away, whilst still warm.

 DAIRY LOVERS

If you have a few cheese lovers in the house then, using a potato peeler, peel some parmesan cheese shavings and add them to the salad, just before serving.

TIP

• This is also sufficient for a light meal or a lunchtime snack. Depending on how big everyone's appetites are, just add more or less bacon per person.

Cherry tomato tart

4 people
10 minutes
40 minutes

INGREDIENTS

210g ready-made puff pastry
(ie, one frozen sheet) – check
it is dairy free. The frozen
varieties are usually fine

1 egg yolk

2-3 red onions (250-300g),
peeled and finely sliced

2 sprigs of thyme (optional)

120g bag of rocket leaves

16 cherry tomatoes, cut in half

A little olive oil

4 tablespoons of balsamic vinegar

OPTIONAL

Balsamic-dressed salad leaves
(120g bag of salad)

TIP

- You can either make one large tart or small individual tarts using mini flan tins.
- If you make individual ones, you may need to reduce the cooking time slightly.

METHOD

1 Preheat the oven to 180°C for a fan oven.

2 Fry the onion in a little olive oil until soft but not coloured. Add the balsamic vinegar and cook for about 10-15 minutes on a slow heat until the mixture takes on a lovely glazed appearance and all the excess liquid has evaporated.

3 Add about a half of the rocket leaves and cook for about 2 minutes until the rocket is wilted. Allow to cool until you are ready to make the tarts.

4 Roll out the puff pastry in a rectangle. Use a knife to lightly score along all 4 edges of the pastry. The marks should be 3-4 cm apart and be careful not to cut right through. Where the pastry is scored it will rise when cooked, giving it a nice upturned look!

5 Spread the onions evenly on the pastry keeping within the scored lines. Cut the tomatoes in half and arrange on top, seeded side facing up.

6 Take the thyme and with your finger and thumb tear the leaves from the stalk and sprinkle on the tart. You can use a teaspoonful of dried thyme if you prefer.

7 Beat the egg yolk and use this to glaze the edges of the pastry, where you have scored it. This will give it a nice colour when it is cooked.

8 Bake in the preheated oven for around 20 minutes until the pastry is cooked and nicely browned.

9 Remove from the oven. Use the rest of the rocket to garnish the tarts.

10 Either serve on its own or with balsamic-dressed salad leaves.

TIP

• **For dairy lovers:** use 25g soft rind goats cheese per person, such as Welsh or Somerset. Remove top and bottom rinds. Put a slice of goat's cheese on the top of each mini flan case and cook as above.

Staple foods
pastas & risottos

INSIDE THIS SECTION

Esna, my god daughter with her brothers, Brennie and Josh helping out. Looks like it's spaghetti tonight!

TIP

• If I am making a pasta dish, I usually make extra sauce and then have it the next day with a different type of pasta – such as farfalle or spaghetti

Pasta with tomato sauce

 4 people **5** minutes **60** minutes

INGREDIENTS

A little olive oil

1 medium red onion, chopped

1-2 garlic cloves, chopped

500g passata

500ml vegetable stock

Half a teaspoon of sugar

Splash of dry martini

2 teaspoons fresh thyme

2 bay leaves

Black pepper to taste

Allow 75-100g of dried pasta
per person

METHOD

1 In a large pan, heat the olive oil and sweat the onion and garlic for a few minutes until soft.

2 Then add all the other ingredients except the black pepper.

3 Cover and simmer for at least an hour, on a low heat, stirring now and then.

4 Season to taste.

5 Serve with the pasta of your choice. A short-dried pasta such as farfalle is great.

 DAIRY LOVERS

You can sprinkle grated parmesan cheese on top of the sauce just before serving.

TIP

• Serve with pasta or use as the base for vegetable bakes.

• If you haven't any passata (ie, sieved tomatoes, you can use a dessertspoon of tomato purée instead)

Pasta all'amatriciana

 4 people

 10 minutes

 35-40 minutes

INGREDIENTS

A little olive oil

2 medium red onions, chopped

150g pancetta or unsmoked bacon, chopped

1 fresh hot red chilli, chopped

175ml white wine

2 x 400g tins chopped tomatoes

Salt and pepper to taste

Add a teaspoonful of dry martini (optional)

Allow 75–100g dried pasta per person

METHOD

1   In a large pan, heat the olive oil and cook the onion for a few minutes until translucent.

2   Add the chopped pancetta and the chilli and stir for 4-5 minutes until the fat of the pancetta becomes translucent.

3   Add the white wine and boil for about 5 minutes to reduce the liquid.

4   Once the liquid has reduced, add the tomatoes.

5   Cover and cook over a moderate heat for about 30 minutes, stirring from time to time.

6   Season with salt and pepper.

7   Serve with the pasta of your choice. But short dried pasta is great.

TIP

• The sauce also tastes great with spaghetti. And for the dairy lovers, add some grated (hard) pecorino romano cheese.

Pasta with bacon, prawns
and rocket

4 people   10 minutes   15 minutes

INGREDIENTS

Allow 75g-100g dried pasta
    such as pappardelle or farfalla
    per person

Salt

1 tablespoon of olive oil

1 garlic clove, chopped

200g pancetta or smoked bacon,
    chopped small

25 large prawns

100ml dry white wine

250g small ripe cherry tomatoes,
    cut in half

1 tablespoon tomato purée

100g rocket

Pepper to taste

METHOD

1   Cook the pasta in plenty of salted boiling water.

2   Heat the olive oil in a frying pan and sauté the garlic until golden.

3   Add the chopped bacon and prawns and cook for 2 minutes and then add the wine, tomatoes and tomato purée.

4   Season with a little salt and cook for about 10 minutes, until some of the liquid has evaporated and the sauce is thicker.

5   Add the rocket and cook for a further 2-3 minutes until the rocket is wilted and cooked through.

6   Drain the cooked pasta, mix with the sauce, season to taste and serve immediately.

TIP

• This will become an instant favourite. The taste of the bacon and the prawns together with the rocket is just amazing!

• Serve with a glass of ice cold sauvignon blanc!

Asparagus risotto

 4 people

 5-10 minutes

 30 minutes

INGREDIENTS

450g asparagus

3 tablespoons olive oil

1 red onion, finely chopped

1 bay leaf

350g of risotto rice, such as Arborio rice

350ml white wine

1 litre vegetable stock

Salt and pepper to taste

METHOD

1 Discard the tough ends of the asparagus and keep the asparagus tips for the risotto.

2 In a saucepan, heat the olive oil and sauté the chopped onion with the bay leaf over a moderate heat for about 7 minutes until the onion is translucent. Add the asparagus tips and cook for 5 minutes until the asparagus starts to soften. Keep stirring to prevent sticking.

3 Add the rice, stirring well to coat the grains. Simmer for 3 minutes then add the white wine.

4 Make your vegetable stock and keep it gently simmering in another pan.

5 When the white wine is absorbed add the hot stock a ladleful at a time. Cook slowly on a moderate heat, topping up with stock to keep the rice from sticking.

6 After about 18-20 minutes the grains of rice should be plump, but not soggy.

7 Remove from the heat and season to taste. Remove the bay leaf. Let it stand for a minute before serving.

 DAIRY LOVERS

You can sprinkle with parmesan cheese for those who are dairy lovers!

Enjoying a meal with my friends in Nairobi, Kenya

...and I even had my hair braided whilst in Nairobi!!

Mushroom risotto

4 people — **10** minutes — **30** minutes

plus 30 minutes standing time

INGREDIENTS

25g dried porcini mushrooms

1 litre vegetable stock

3 tablespoons olive oil

1 red onion, finely chopped

75g white cup mushrooms

350g risotto rice, such as
    Arborio rice

350ml white wine

1 bay leaf

Salt and pepper to taste

METHOD

1   Soak the dried porcini in 500ml hot water for about
    30 minutes.

2   Meanwhile, in a saucepan make up the vegetable stock
    with 500ml of water and leave to simmer gently.

3   Drain the porcini but retain the liquid and add it to the
    vegetable stock, so that you have about 1 litre of stock
    for your risotto.

4   In another saucepan heat the olive oil and sauté the
    chopped onion over a moderate heat for about 7 minutes
    until the onion is translucent. Add the mushrooms and
    cook for 3-5 minutes.

5   Add the rice, stirring well to coat the grains with oil.
    Simmer for 3 minutes then add the white wine.

6   When the white wine is absorbed add the bay leaf and
    then the hot stock a ladleful at a time. Cook slowly on
    a moderate heat and keep topping up with stock,
    otherwise it will stick.

7   After about 18-20 minutes the grains of rice should
    be plump, but not soggy.

8   Remove from the heat and season to taste. Discard the
    bay leaf. Let it stand for a minute before serving.

 DAIRY LOVERS

You can sprinkle with parmesan cheese
for those who are dairy lovers!

TIP

• Risotto needs to be made
with the right kind of rice.
It must be Arborio, Carnaroli
or Vialone Nano, which are
stubby in appearance and
have an almost nutty flavour
when cooked.

Feeling hungry?

main meals

INSIDE THIS SECTION

DON'T FORGET THE WINE!

WHITE WINE: You can't go wrong with a Sauvignon Blanc from New Zealand – Marlborough wines are particularly good.

RED WINE: Go for a Shiraz or Merlot from South Africa or a Rioja, depending on your menu.

When I was going through chemo, I found that red wine tasted like cough mixture and white wine like vinegar. But I did find champagne still tasted okay! So just go for what you like!

TIP

● Serve these delicious mains with chunky chips, sweet mash, or rice – ring the changes and don't forget the veg!

Baked ham and eggs

 4 people

 5 minutes

 15-20 minutes

INGREDIENTS

4 slices of baked ham or smoked ham for a richer taste

4 medium-sized eggs

200g spinach (optional)

Salt and pepper to taste

METHOD

1 Preheat the oven to 180°C for a fan oven.

2 Lightly grease a scone or muffin tin and then arrange a slice of ham in each separate muffin/scone holder.

3 Break one egg into each section over the ham and bake in the oven for around 15 minutes or until the eggs are cooked through.

4 Meanwhile, if you are using it, steam the spinach for around 5 minutes until cooked and squeeze out the excess water before serving.

5 Serve each ham and egg on a bed of spinach.

TIP

• **This is** really easy **to do and everyone loves it. I often serve this as a quick snack on a Saturday lunchtime just before the football starts – wouldn't want to get in the way of the football!**

• **For a** more substantial **meal, just add some fresh bread or a slice of wholemeal toast, with dairy-free spread of course!**

Lenny and baby Marley are, as you can see avid Chelsea fans! Quick the football is starting...

Salmon fillets
with a tomato sauce

4 people   **10** minutes   **40** minutes

INGREDIENTS

A little olive oil

2 large onions

500ml of vegetable stock

1 tablespoon red wine

1 400g tin tomatoes

1 tablespoon tomato purée or
    for a more intense flavour
    sun-dried tomato paste

Half a teaspoon of sugar

4 skinless salmon fillets

METHOD

1   Preheat the oven to 180°C for a fan oven.

2   Chop the onion finely and cook in a little olive oil until soft but not coloured.

3   Add the vegetable stock, red wine, tomatoes, tomato purée and sugar, and cook for about 15 minutes until the liquid has mostly evaporated.

4   Place salmon fillets in an ovenproof casserole dish. Pour the sauce over the fillets and cook with the lid on for 20 minutes in a preheated oven.

5   Serve with a green salad or green beans and chunky chips, if feeling hungry, naughty or both!

This recipe is also great with chicken. Use skinless chicken breasts instead of the salmon. Make the sauce as above. Then add a little olive oil to a frying pan and gently brown the chicken on both sides. Place the chicken in an ovenproof dish with a lid and pour the sauce over it. Cook for 30 minutes in a preheated oven. Make sure the chicken is fully cooked through. Serve with rice, green salad or chunky chips.

TIP

• By cooking the salmon in a casserole dish with a fitted lid, you don't get the house smelling of fish for days!

Salmon Wellington

4 people · 10 minutes · 20 minutes

INGREDIENTS

500g puff pastry (check it is dairy free. The frozen type is usually okay as it is made with vegetable oil rather than butter)

4 skinless salmon fillets

4 cherry tomatoes, thinly sliced

2 tablespoons of lemon juice, plus wedges to serve

1 egg, beaten

GREEN PESTO

2 large handfuls of fresh basil leaves (40g)

4 tablespoons olive oil

40g pine kernels

2 cloves garlic, peeled and crushed

Salt to taste

TIP

• Pesto keeps for weeks in the fridge. Cover it with a layer of olive oil in a small jar. Bang the jar on a table to get rid of any air bubbles.

METHOD

1. Preheat oven to 180°C for a fan oven.

2. Firstly make the green pesto. Whizz the basil with the olive oil, pine kernels and garlic in a food processor. Add salt to taste. You do need to make your own pesto as shop bought varieties virtually all have pecorini or parmesan cheese as a main ingredient.

3. Roll out half the pastry to a large rectangle, then cut it into 4 smaller rectangles – one for each fillet.

4. Spread equal amounts of the pesto over the centre of each rectangle, leaving a 3cm pastry border. Place a salmon fillet on top, season, then lay slices of tomato on the fish. Drizzle with the lemon juice and brush the pastry border with some beaten egg.

5. Roll out the other pastry into a slightly wider rectangle and cut it into 4 smaller rectangles. Make 3-4 lengthways slits, close together in the centre of each rectangle, then lay it on top of the salmon fillet – pull the pastry slightly to separate the slits, but don't tear it. Press the pastry borders together to seal, use the back of a knife to make the edges look nice, then trim to neaten each parcel.

6. Brush each parcel all over with beaten egg, then put them on a non-stick baking tray or a tray lined with baking paper.

7. Bake for 20 minutes in the preheated oven, until the pastry is puffed and golden.

SERVING SUGGESTION

Serve with a green salad. This is very filling so you don't need any potatoes with it!

Baked salmon with olives

4 people

10 minutes

25 minutes

INGREDIENTS

200g green beans or asparagus
   or a mixture of the two

4 skinless salmon fillets

2 lemons

Salt and pepper to taste

A little olive oil

1 handful of fresh basil

20-25 black pitted olives

20 small cherry tomatoes,
   cut in half

4 sun-dried tomatoes, chopped

12 anchovy fillets

METHOD

1. Preheat the oven to 180°C for a fan oven.

2. Top and tail the green beans and, if using asparagus, snap off the tough ends of the stalks. Then steam the vegetables for 4-5 minutes or until tender.

3. Meanwhile, give the salmon fillets a quick wash under the tap and pat dry with kitchen paper. Squeeze the juice of half a lemon over each fillet, on both sides, then season with salt and pepper. Place in the centre of an ovenproof dish and drizzle a little olive oil over the top of each salmon fillet.

4. Then place the basil, olives and tomatoes at one side of the salmon fillets. Cut the sun-dried tomatoes into small pieces and mix in with the tomatoes. Keep a few pieces over and place on top of the salmon. Drizzle with a little olive oil.

5. Put the green beans and/or asparagus at the other side of the salmon fillets and place the anchovies on top.

6. Roast in the preheated oven for 20 minutes or until cooked through.

TIP

• If you can only buy salmon fillets with the skins on, then don't worry, just use a very sharp knife to remove the skin.

Mediterranean baked cod

4 people

5-10 minutes

15-20 minutes

INGREDIENTS

600g cod fillets – 1 fillet per person

6 sun-dried tomatoes, chopped

2 tablespoons sun-dried tomato paste

20 black olives, pitted and sliced

400g tin chopped tomatoes

METHOD

1 Preheat the oven to180°C for a fan oven.

2 Place the cod fillets in an ovenproof dish. Mix together the sun-dried tomatoes, sun-dried tomato paste, olives and chopped tomatoes and spread the mixture over the cod fillets.

3 Bake in the oven for 15-20 minutes or until piping hot.

4 Serve with green beans.

 DAIRY LOVERS

For those who like cheese, just make a separate dish as above but sprinkle with parmesan before baking.

If you have some left over tapenade (see page 29) you can use this instead of the black olives. Add around 2 tablespoons of the tapenade and mix in with the tomatoes. It is really tasty as the capers in the tapenade give it a bit of a kick!

TIP

• I find frozen fish best as it doesn't seem to smell the house out like fresh fish does! Fully defrost the fish before cooking.

Shopping for our local produce to go with our baked cod

Pork and apricot casserole

4 people | **10** minutes | **75** minutes

plus 30 minutes standing time

INGREDIENTS

100g ready to eat dried apricots, roughly chopped

50g dried apples, roughly chopped

150ml dry white wine

Olive oil

4 pork chops or 500g pork fillet, cut into bite-size chunks

1 medium onion, chopped

2 whole cloves

1 teaspoon ground cinnamon

500ml chicken stock

Salt and pepper to taste

METHOD

1 Preheat the oven to 200°C for a fan oven.

2 Soak the apricots and apples in the white wine, adding a little water to cover, if necessary, for around 30 minutes.

3 In a frying pan, heat a little olive oil and brown the meat all over. Put the meat into a casserole dish and cover. Then lightly fry the onions until soft and add them to the casserole dish.

4 Add the soaked dried fruits and the spices to the casserole and stir. Then add the chicken stock and stir well to combine.

5 Put the casserole into the preheated oven and cook until the mixture is bubbling.

6 Then turn down to 180°C and cook for 1¼ hours, until everything is tender. The meat should literally melt in your mouth.

7 Serve with green beans or spinach.

TIP

• The mix of flavours in this dish is stunning. This is now a firm favourite of my mum and dad who make it every week.

Beef casserole

6 people

20 minutes

150 minutes

The borlotti beans are a great source of protein and help this dish to go that bit further for hungry people!

INGREDIENTS

A little olive oil

2 red onions, chopped

Half a bunch of spring onions

1 garlic clove, chopped

3 carrots, chopped

3 leeks, sliced

75g green beans, to 4cm lengths

12 button mushrooms

Bouquet garni

Salt and pepper to taste

500ml beef stock

100g bacon, diced

500g diced braising steak

150ml red wine

410g tin borlotti beans (optional)

Juice of half a lemon

Sprig of parsley for decoration (optional)

TIP

- This can be made the day before and then reheated slowly in a saucepan.
- Serve with basmati rice or chunky chips or roast potatoes.

METHOD

1   Preheat the oven to 200°C for a fan oven.

2   Heat a little olive oil in a large saucepan, add the onions and garlic, and cook until soft.

3   Add the carrots, leeks, green beans, mushrooms and sweat them over a low heat for 5-10 minutes, adding more olive oil if required to prevent the vegetables from sticking.

4   Transfer the vegetables to a large casserole dish. Add bouquet garni, salt, pepper and the beef stock. Put the lid on and leave to one side.

5   Using a high heat, add around 2 tablespoons of olive oil to the same saucepan and add the diced bacon and meat a little at a time until it changes colour and is sealed on all sides. Once the meat is browned transfer it to the casserole dish. Add the red wine to the saucepan to loosen any meat sediment then add it to the casserole.

6   If you are using them, drain the borlotti beans, rinse in water and then add them to the casserole.

7   Cover and put the casserole in the preheated oven and bring back to boiling point. Then turn the oven down to 160°C for a fan oven and cook slowly for another 2-2½ hours.

8   Just before serving, add the juice of half a lemon and if the gravy needs thickening mix up some gravy powder with a little cold water and add to the casserole. Bring it back to the boil and cook through for a further 5-10 minutes.

9   Serve with a decorative sprig of parsley as a finishing touch!

Don't worry if you haven't got any bacon. Just make the recipe without. The bacon adds extra taste, but the casserole tastes fine with just the braising steak.

Chicken casserole

 4 people

 15 minutes

 70 minutes

INGREDIENTS

A little olive oil

Salt and pepper to taste

3-4 skinless chicken breasts

2 red onions, finely chopped

1 garlic clove, crushed

400g tin tomatoes

100ml vegetable stock

Half a teaspoon of paprika

2 red, yellow, or orange peppers,
    deseeded and chopped

2 bay leaves

150ml dry white wine

METHOD

1   Preheat the oven to 180°C for a fan oven.

2   Add a little olive oil in a large saucepan, season the chicken breasts and then fry for 5-6 minutes until golden, turning regularly to prevent sticking. Remove the chicken and set to one side.

3   Add a little more olive oil and cook the chopped onions and garlic for about 4-5 minutes, until soft.

4   Add the tomatoes, vegetable stock, paprika, peppers, bay leaves, white wine and seasoning.

5   Bring to the boil and stir well. Then transfer to a casserole dish, add the browned chicken pieces, cover and cook in the preheated oven for one hour.

6   Don't forget to remove the bay leaves before serving.

TIP

• This works really well if you serve it with green beans and chunky chips or sweet potatoes.

• For a richer taste add a dessertspoon of tomato purée when cooking.

Esna & Brennie in South Africa on safari. Wrapped up looking forward to a warming supper of chicken casserole!

Chicken and bean stew

4 people

10 minutes

35-40 minutes

This is a great dish as it can all be cooked in one saucepan on the top of the stove, so less washing up!

INGREDIENTS

Olive oil

2 red onions, chopped

Half a bunch of spring onions

1 garlic clove, chopped

4 rashers of smoked back bacon, finely chopped

3-4 skinless chicken breasts, chopped into about 8 pieces each

2 leeks, sliced

75g green beans, chopped into 4cm lengths

12 button mushrooms

500ml vegetable stock

1 dessertspoon tomato purée

2 teaspoons dry martini

Bouquet garni

410g tin borlotti beans

Salt and pepper to taste

METHOD

1   Heat a little olive oil in a large saucepan, add the onions and garlic, and cook until soft.

2   Add the bacon and fry for 2-3 minutes, then the chicken pieces and cook for a further 4-5 minutes, turning regularly until they begin to brown.

3   Add the chopped leeks, green beans and mushrooms, the vegetable stock, tomato purée, martini and the bouquet garni.

4   Drain the borlotti beans, rinse in cold water and then add to the dish.

5   Simmer for 30 minutes or until the chicken is cooked through and the sauce has reduced to a thick consistency. Season to taste.

6   Serve with basmati rice, or sweet potatoes.

TIP

• If you want a more tomato taste, then add a 400g tin of chopped tomatoes along with the vegetables.

Thai chicken curry

4 people | 10 minutes | 30 minutes

INGREDIENTS

4 shallots, peeled and roughly chopped

1cm piece of ginger

2 stalks of lemon grass

2 tablespoons of groundnut oil (or sunflower oil)

Bunch of coriander

3 limes

3-4 teaspoons of Thai green curry paste (this is what makes it hot, so add to taste!)

1 tin of coconut milk (ideally use the half fat variety)

200ml chicken stock

2 skinless chicken breasts, cut into small chunks

175g petit pois (you can use frozen but cook them separately before adding to recipe if you do)

4 teaspoons of Thai fish sauce

TIP

• This can be made the day before and reheated. But don't add the chicken until you are ready to eat and serve.

METHOD

1 Place the shallots, ginger, lemon grass, groundnut oil, coriander into a blender with the juice of one lime. Blend to a smooth paste.

2 Add the curry paste and blend again.

3 In a saucepan, add the paste and fry over a medium heat for 2-3 minutes until cooked through but not browned. Pour in the coconut milk and chicken stock. Bring the mixture to a gentle simmer and then allow to cook for 15 minutes on a slow heat, half covering the pan with the lid.

4 Add the chicken pieces and the peas and cook for another 10 minutes or until cooked through. Stir in the fish sauce and the juice of 2 limes and cook for a further 2 minutes.

5 Serve with rice. For the posh restaurant look, put the rice in a cup, turn it upside down and place the cup-shaped rice onto the serving plate. Arrange the curry sauce around the edge of the rice.

When I first made this dish I was on my second bout of chemo and had lost much of my taste, with everything tasting of metal. So I overdid the green curry paste. Even though it was a very cold December day by the end of lunch everyone was in their shirt sleeves or T shirts. Even my niece who was over from Dubai and hates the cold took her coat off! So if you are going through chemo... get someone else to check the taste first!

TIP

• This looks fiddly, but it is just a longer list of ingredients. The smell of fresh lemon grass cooking is fab. You can freeze lemon grass, so if you buy enough for 2 meals, you can freeze the rest for another day.

A bit on the side
get your five-a-day

INSIDE THIS SECTION

TIP

• Whether you are looking for real **comfort food** such as chunky chips and sweet potato mash or want to **liven up those** sad-looking carrots that have been sitting at the bottom of the fridge! Then these recipes are for you!

Chunky chips
and chunky sweet potato

4 people | 5 minutes | 20-25 minutes

These are really easy to make, as the potatoes are only scrubbed and not peeled, and the crusty skins are always a favourite with everyone.

INGREDIENTS

6 large old potatoes,
   e.g. golden wonder

Olive oil or beef dripping

Sea salt to taste

METHOD

1 Preheat the oven to 200°C for a fan oven.

2 Scrub the potatoes well and cut into quarters lengthways then into chips that are about 2cm thick.

3 Put them into a roasting tin, drizzle with olive oil and toss so they are barely coated with the oil.

4 Roast in the preheated oven for 20-25 minutes depending on the size of the chips.

5 Sprinkle with sea salt and serve immediately.

CHUNKY SWEET POTATO ALTERNATIVE

Using sweet potatoes is also great. Take 3 sweet potatoes, peeled and cut into eight pieces or chunks about 4cm by 2cm and follow the recipe above. Many of my friends prefer the taste to white potatoes. Try it and see!

SERVING SUGGESTION

For a spicier taste for either sweet potatoes or white potatoes, add a quarter teaspoon of ground cumin and a quarter teaspoon of ground cinnamon. Mix the spices together and then sprinkle them over the potatoes with the olive oil. Shake the roasting tin to toss everything together and cook as above.

TIP

• Add a few sprigs of fresh rosemary with the olive oil and cook as above.

• Great with roast chicken.

Juicy carrots

 4 people

 10 minutes

 15 minutes

INGREDIENTS

500g carrots peeled

1 orange

METHOD

1 Peel the carrots and cut each carrot lengthways into quarters.

2 Bring a pan of water to the boil, add the carrots and cook them for 12-15 minutes. Or you could steam them.

3 Squeeze the juice of half an orange.

4 Drain the cooked carrots and lightly sprinkle with the juice from the orange. This gives the carrots a really sweet taste.

5 Don't overdo the orange juice! Add a bit at a time, and taste until you are happy with the flavour!

TIP

• For a posh look, cut the carrots into tiny match sticks – called **julienne strips**.

All-in-one winter vegetables

4 people · 5 minutes · 45 minutes

INGREDIENTS

400g small carrots, peeled and cut lengthways into even-sized pieces

400g small parsnips, peeled and cut into even-sized pieces, sliced lengthways

350g small red potatoes, unpeeled, cut into 8 pieces

1 medium red onion, cut into slices

6 tablespoons French vinaigrette

1 bay leaf

Salt and pepper to taste

METHOD

1 Preheat the oven to 180°C for a fan oven.

2 Toss the prepared vegetables in the vinaigrette dressing and add the bay leaf.

3 Fold a piece of foil in half and lay one half along the length of a roasting tray, and lay all the vegetables on the foil. Then fold the foil over to make a parcel. Seal it all round. You should end up with a parcel that exactly fits the tray but with some air space between the foil and the vegetables.

4 Cook in the preheated oven for 45 minutes.

5 Remove the bay leaf and serve.

TIP

• Don't forget to remove the bay leaves before serving, as the leaves, despite cooking, stay thin, rigid and sharp so you don't want to accidentally eat one and hurt your throat!

Sweet potato mash

4 people

5 minutes

15-20 minutes

INGREDIENTS

2 sweet potatoes, peeled and cut
    into even-sized pieces

A little olive oil

Salt and pepper to taste

METHOD

1   Boil or steam the sweet potatoes for about 15 minutes or until soft.

2   Drain the potatoes and mash with a little olive oil using a potato masher until smooth.

OPTIONAL SUGGESTION

You can also add in some cauliflower to give a slightly different flavour, using around 1 part cauliflower to 2 parts sweet potato.

TIP

• This is great on its own, or as a **topping** on dishes such as cottage pie, instead of using ordinary potato.

Root mash

 4 people

 10 minutes

 25 minutes

INGREDIENTS

900g mixed root vegetables,
    such as swede, parsnips,
    carrots, celeriac, sweet potato
    – cut into chunks

1 dessertspoon olive oil

Salt and pepper to taste

1 teaspoon dried thyme or
    1 tablespoon of chopped
    fresh thyme

METHOD

1   Peel the vegetables and cut into chunks.

2   Place in a large saucepan of cold salted water and bring
    to the boil. Then simmer for 15-20 minutes until tender.

3   Drain the vegetables, then mash with olive oil.
    Stir in the thyme and season to taste.

TIP

• Use the veg to make a great vegetable soup see the soup recipe on page 12 which just tells you how to make any soup, ie, 1, 1 and 3 parts.

Parsnips and honey

4 people

10-15 minutes

45-50 minutes

INGREDIENTS

1kg parsnips, peeled

A little olive oil

10g fresh thyme, leaves only

1 tablespoon of honey

Salt and pepper to taste

METHOD

1 Preheat the oven to 180°C for a fan oven.

2 Cut the parsnips in half lengthways.

3 Bring a pan of water to the boil and add the parsnips. Parboil for 10 minutes until they are soft but not mushy then drain.

4 Toss with the olive oil and thyme, then coat in the honey and add salt and pepper to taste.

5 Lay the parsnips flat in a hot roasting tin and roast for about 35-40 minutes until golden.

TIP

Roast parsnips are delicious and the honey makes them extra sweet. Perfect with a roast dinner.

Steamed broccolli
with lemon

4 people

5 minutes

5-10 minutes

INGREDIENTS

1 large head of broccoli

1 unwaxed lemon – zest and juice only

1 dessertspoon olive oil

Salt and pepper to taste

METHOD

1 Cut the broccoli into about 8 small pieces, discarding any woody stalks.

2 Steam for around 5-10 minutes until cooked, but not soft or mushy.

3 Grate the rind from the lemon and squeeze it for the juice.

4 Mix the steamed broccoli with the lemon zest and lemon juice and a little olive oil in a bowl. Season to taste and serve.

TIP
• This is really great with grilled or baked salmon.

Mange tout and baby peas

 4 people

 5 minutes

 10 minutes

INGREDIENTS

120g mange tout or sugar snaps,
  cut into thin strips

A little olive oil

275ml frozen baby peas/petit pois

Salt and pepper to taste

METHOD

1 Toss the mange tout in the olive oil and steam them for 5 minutes.

2 Add the frozen baby peas or petit pois and steam for a further 3 minutes or until cooked.

3 Season to taste and serve.

Smile and eat up!

TIP

• This has a **lovely sweet taste**. You may even get the kids to like vegetables with this dish!

Blinis

 4 people **10** minutes **10** minutes

I call these, poor man's blinis, as they use potato as their main base. I love them and they go down a treat as a snack, on their own, or served with dips.

INGREDIENTS

4 spring onions, chopped

1 garlic clove

A little olive oil

2 rashers of back bacon, finely chopped

3 medium potatoes, peeled and coarsely grated

2 eggs

50g flour

Salt and pepper to taste

4 chives, cut into small pieces

METHOD

1 Preheat the oven to 180°C for a fan oven.

2 Chop the onion and garlic finely and cook over a low heat with a little olive oil, using a non-stick frying pan for about 2 minutes. Then add the bacon and cook for a further 5 minutes or until cooked. Allow to cool before adding to the potato mixture.

3 Peel the potatoes and then grate using the coarser side of the grater. Beat one egg (leave the other egg for later) and then add to the potatoes and mix through.

4 Add the flour, salt and chives to the potato mixture and mix well until blended.

5 Take the other egg and separate the white and the yolk, keeping just the egg white. In a separate bowl, whisk the egg white until fluffy but not stiff. Add this to the potato mixture and blend it well in.

6 Heat the olive oil in a large frying pan. Fry small spoonfuls of the mixture in the hot oil, turning only once when the first side is well browned. Cook the other side until done.

7 Keep the cooked blinis hot in the oven while cooking the rest.

These can be made in advance and then reheated in a preheated oven at 180°C for a fan oven, for about 10 minutes.

TIP

• Grated potatoes discolour very quickly, so they must be used straight away.

Tagine of chickpeas

 4 people

 30 minutes

 45-50 minutes

I occasionally have just this as a main meal, or if I have my fitness crew around, who are always hungry after training, then I make it as a side dish.

A bit on the side get your five-a-day

INGREDIENTS

3 tablespoons olive oil

1 onion, chopped

1 garlic clove, finely chopped

Quarter teaspoon cayenne pepper

Half teaspoon paprika

Quarter teaspoon ground ginger

Half teaspoon ground turmeric

1 teaspoon ground cumin

1 teaspoon ground cinnamon

400g tin chopped tomatoes

1 teaspoon sugar

Salt and pepper to taste

2 x 420g tins chickpeas

1 large potato cut into chunks

3 tablespoons, flat leaf Italian parsley, chopped

2 tablespoons coriander leaves, chopped

METHOD

1   Put the olive oil and onion in a large saucepan and cook over a medium heat for 5-6 minutes or until softened.

2   Stir in the garlic, cayenne pepper and spices and cook gently for 2-3 minutes.

3   Add the tomatoes and sugar and season to taste. Cover and simmer for 20 minutes.

4   Meanwhile, drain the chickpeas and put them in a large bowl with enough cold water to cover them well. Lift up handfuls of chickpeas and rub them between your hands to loosen the skins. Run more water into the bowl, stir well and let
the skins float to the top, then skim them off. Repeat until all the skins have been removed.

5   Drain the chickpeas again and stir them into the tomato mixture. Cut the potatoes into small chunks and them add as well. Cover and simmer for 20-25 minutes, adding a little more water if necessary.

6   Stir in the parsley and coriander and season to taste.

7   Serve with crusty bread.

TIP

• **Skinned chickpeas** are better as they absorb the flavours. But if you don't have time to do this, then just leave the skins on. Or if you have some chickpeas left over then use them to make **hummus** – see page 24.

This sounds a bit fiddly but once you have bought all your jars of spices, you are virtually there and the flavours work really well together.

Keep 'em sweet
desserts

Baby Josh – working up an appetite for supper!

The Venters on safari and tucking into a mid-morning snack...

...muffins! Get 'em they're gone! Pa

Feelin' fit 'n fruity!
Turn to page 78

Suzi and James my godchildren having a good time...

Josh, my great nephew, enjoying helping m to make strawberries dipped in chocolat

by Allegra and mum on holiday
in Majorca – what's for supper?

Sal and me tucking in!
Well it is the weekend!

INSIDE THIS SECTION

TIP

• **For** simple and delicious desserts**, any of these recipes can be prepared in advance so go on, treat yourself.**

Posh pancakes

4 people

10 minutes

10 minutes

plus 120 minutes standing time

I don't know about you, but Pancake Tuesday without pancakes just doesn't work. But this tastes great and so you don't need to miss out on that treat! And there is a special variation on the next page so you can also eat them at Christmas!

INGREDIENTS

500ml plain white flour

Pinch of salt

1 tablespoon caster sugar

1 teaspoon grated orange zest and
    1 tablespoon orange juice

4 medium-sized eggs

500ml water

25ml Grand Marnier or Cointreau
    (optional)

60ml melted Pure (dairy-free
    spread) or use olive oil instead

TO SERVE

Juice of 1 lemon

Caster sugar

METHOD

1 Blend all the ingredients together in a food processor, except the melted dairy-free spread or olive oil. The mixture should have a smooth consistency with no lumps.

2 Transfer the batter to a jug with a lid on and put it in the fridge for at least 2 hours. It is fine for it to stand overnight in the fridge.

3 Just before use, add the melted butter or olive oil (if using olive oil there is no need to heat the olive oil, just pour it directly into the batter). Dilute the batter with more water if too thick. It should have the consistency of thin cream.

4 Using a small non-stick frying pan, lightly wipe the pan with a little olive oil. Just use the mearest trace of oil, to prevent the pancakes from sticking. Get the pan really hot, then turn the heat down to medium and, aiming for the centre of the pan, pour in the batter using a soup spoon so that you use the same amount of batter every time. (2 tablespoons is about right for an 18cm pan.) Angle the hot pan back and forth to spread the batter evenly over the entire surface. It should only take half a minute or so to cook the pancake and you will see small bubbles forming on the batter as it is cooking. Flip the pancake over with a palette knife and once it is golden brown slide it onto a plate to keep warm. The pancakes should be very thin.

5 Stack the pancakes as you make them between sheets of greaseproof paper on a heated plate, and put them in the oven to keep warm whilst you make the rest of the pancakes.

6 Serve with caster sugar and lemon juice, or add the mincemeat sauce as detailed on next page.

TIP

• Pancakes freeze well, but should be separated by pieces of greaseproof paper. They may also be refrigerated for up to two days.

Christmas pancakes

 4 people

 10 minutes

 10 minutes

INGREDIENTS

6 tablespoons sweet mincemeat

2 teaspoons orange zest

Juice of 2 oranges

2 tablespoons Grand Marnier
or Cointreau

METHOD

1   Make the pancakes as described on previous page.

2   In a small saucepan heat the mincemeat. Then spread around one dessertspoon of mincemeat over each pancake and fold. Put in an ovenproof dish and place in a heated oven to keep warm.

3   Mix the orange zest and orange juice together and heat gently. Then pour over the pancakes and return to the oven, to keep warm. Just before serving pour the Grand Marnier or Cointreau over the pancakes. Light a match, stand back and light the alcohol. Once the flames have gone out, serve immediately. I often serve this instead of christmas pudding, as it has a Christmas feel, but is not too filling.

TIP

• Pancakes can be reheated by warming in the oven for around 10 minutes at 180⁰C for a fan oven.

Fruit in dark chocolate
with fresh fruit coulis

 4 people   **10** minutes   **10** minutes

INGREDIENTS

12 strawberries

Half a melon

Half a pineapple

100g Lindt 70% dark chocolate
(dairy free)

FOR THE FRUIT COULIS (OPTIONAL)

450g mixed berries, ie,
strawberries, raspberries,
blackberries & redcurrants

200g caster sugar

200ml water

METHOD

1 Cut the melon into small slices, the strawberries into two and the pineapple into chunks.

2 Place the chocolate broken into squares into a heatproof bowl and place it over a pan of simmering water. Allow the chocolate to melt over a very gentle heat.

3 Try not to eat too much chocolate yourself! Leave some for the fruit!

4 Dip the fruit into the chocolate and place on baking paper until the chocolate sets.

OPTIONAL FRUIT COULIS

1 Wash the fruits.

2 Heat the sugar and water gently until the liquid is completely clear and all the sugar has dissolved.

3 Add the berries and remove the mixture from the heat. Allow it to cool completely before puréeing and then, for a really fine sauce, pass it through a sieve to remove any seeds.

4 Serve on the side with the fruit dipped in chocolate. The mix of the sweet chocolate and the sharp taste of the berries is yummy!

TIP

 • If you have children they love to help with this recipe and it doesn't matter if the fruit has more chocolate on some pieces than others. Just have fun!

Orange slices and Cointreau

 4 people

 10 minutes

 20 minutes

INGREDIENTS

4 oranges, finely peeled and sliced
with the pith removed

1 tablespoon Cointreau

50ml of water, or enough to just
cover the orange slices

1 teaspoon sugar

METHOD

1 Preheat the oven to 180°C for a fan oven.

2 Peel and slice the oranges and place in an ovenproof dish.

3 Add enough water to cover the oranges and add the sugar and the Cointreau.

4 Place in the oven and cook for about 20 minutes.

TIP

• Navel oranges available from November to May are best as they are seedless and peel easily. Valencia oranges can also be used – these are available during the summer months but are often smaller and may have seeds.

If this seems too healthy, make macaroons (see page 83) and serve with coffee after a meal.

Stuffed baked peaches

6 people

10 minutes

30-35 minutes

INGREDIENTS

2 very ripe, yellow peaches, peeled

6 ripe, yellow peaches, halved and stoned

12 Amaretto biscuits, broken into pieces

50g caster sugar

A few drops of lemon juice

A handful of peeled almonds, chopped

METHOD

1 Preheat the oven to 180°C for a fan oven.

2 Place the 2 very ripe peaches in a bowl and mash with a fork until they are completely puréed.

3 Add the broken Amaretto biscuits, half of the sugar and the lemon juice. Work together until the mixture is amalgamated.

4 Place the 6 halved and stoned peaches, cut side up, in an ovenproof dish, lightly greased with olive oil.

5 Fill each peach with the Amaretto mixture. Sprinkle with the almonds and the remaining sugar.

6 Bake in the preheated oven for 30-35 minutes until they are golden on top but still retain their shape.

7 Serve warm or cold.

TIP

• For **dairy lovers** serve with cold Greek yoghurt.

Almond torte

8 people · 10-15 minutes · 45 minutes

This is also delicious made with oranges instead of lemons. Use the recipe below but substitute the grated zest and juice of half an orange instead of the lemon for the torte.

INGREDIENTS

300g ground almonds

4 medium eggs, separated
(you will need both the yolks and the egg whites)

250g caster sugar

Juice and grated zest of
1 unwaxed lemon

1 teaspoon ground cinnamon

Icing sugar to dust

FOR THE LEMON SYRUP

Juice and grated zest of
2 unwaxed lemons

1 teaspoon caster sugar/sugar
to taste

METHOD

1 Preheat the oven to 160°C for a fan oven.

2 Grease a 20cm round loose-bottomed cake tin and line the base with baking paper.

3 Place the 4 egg yolks, sugar, lemon zest and lemon juice in a large bowl and mix with an electric whisk until the mixture becomes thick, creamy and pale. **Do not throw away the egg whites, as you will need them later.**

4 Next add in the ground almonds and cinnamon and mix together.

5 Place the 4 egg whites in a clean bowl and whisk with an electric whisk until they form stiff peaks. Using a metal spoon, lightly fold the egg white a few tablespoons at a time, into the almond mixture until it is fully combined.

6 Pour into the tin and bake in the preheated oven for 45 minutes or until a skewer comes out clean. Leave to cool in the tin.

7 Once cool, remove from tin and dust lightly with icing sugar.

SYRUP

8 Just before serving, finely grate the rind of 2 unwaxed lemons and add with the juice from the 2 lemons to a saucepan. Add the caster sugar and 1 tablespoon of cold water to the saucepan and heat gently. Spoon the warm syrup over the cake and serve immediately.

For the orange variation, use the grated zest of 1 orange and the juice of 1½ oranges. Taste before adding any sugar as oranges can be quite sweet. You can also add a dessertspoon of Cointreau to the syrup to make it very tasty!

TIP
• This recipe is also gluten free so you can have your cake and eat it!

Almond macaroons

8 people · **15** minutes · **20** minutes

INGREDIENTS

175g ground almonds

125g caster sugar

Pinch of salt

1 egg white

1 teaspoon almond extract

Icing sugar for dusting
    (optional)

METHOD

1 Preheat the oven to 160°C for a fan oven.

2 Line a baking tray with baking paper or rice paper.

3 Put the almonds, sugar and salt in a food processor and whizz until finely ground.

4 In a clean bowl, whisk the egg white until it is thick and fluffy using an electric whisk.

5 Add the almond extract to the almond mixture and fold in the egg white. Stir until it forms a smooth paste.

6 Dampen your hands and make about 12 small balls and put them on the baking tray, or use a mini scone tray.

7 Bake in the preheated oven for about 20 minutes until lightly coloured but not brown.

8 Cool on a wire rack and then dust with icing sugar.

TIP

• Great with coffee as a petit four or with fresh fruit to add extra sweetness to the meal.

Quick chocolate tart

6 people

10 minutes

15-20 minutes

INGREDIENTS

100g of Lindt 70% dark chocolate
    (dairy free)

75g Pure dairy-free spread

A dash of olive oil

2 egg yolks and 1 whole egg

50g castor sugar

20cm precooked pastry case
    (check dairy free)

Cocoa powder for dusting

METHOD

1   Preheat the oven to 190°C for a fan oven.

2   Put the chocolate, broken into chunks, the dairy-free spread and a dash of olive oil in a heatproof bowl placed over a pan of very gently simmering water. Stir the mixture as it melts but do not let it boil.

3   In a clean dish, whisk the 2 egg yolks and 2 eggs with the sugar until thick and fluffy using an electric whisk.

4   Turn the pastry case very gently out of its foil case and place it on a baking tray.

5   Slowly pour the melted chocolate into the egg mix and mix in well.

6   Pour the mixture into the pastry case and cook for 10 minutes in the preheated oven.

7   Cool. Then dust with cocoa powder and enjoy!

8   Delicious served with fresh strawberries.

TIP

• **My** teenage friends love this recipe. **It is very easy to make and tastes out of this world, as the middle is all soft and gooey. You can of course use butter for dairy lovers, instead of the Pure spread, which will give it a richer taste.**

Muffins

8-10 muffins · 10 minutes · 25 minutes

INGREDIENTS

150g carrots, peeled and chopped

2 medium-sized eggs

100g dark brown soft sugar
   (raw cane sugar)

3 tablespoons sunflower oil

100g self raising flour

50g desiccated coconut

1 teaspoon ground cinnamon

Half a teaspoon ground nutmeg

50g raisins

METHOD

1 Preheat the oven to 180°C for a fan oven.

2 Whizz the carrots in a food processor until finely chopped. Add the eggs and sugar and whizz until thick and creamy. Slowly add in the oil.

3 Then add the flour, coconut and spices. Stir in the raisins and mix in well. Don't use the food processor for this bit otherwise your raisins will end up chopped too!

4 Using a non-stick muffin tin or scone tin (or muffin cases), spoon the mixture into the individual cases. It should make around 8-10 depending on the size of your muffin tin.

5 Bake in the preheated oven for about 25 minutes until firm and springy to the touch and golden brown.

6 Cool on a wire tray.

TIP

• Get in quick! These rarely last more than an afternoon in my house. They are delicious!

This is me teaching body pump!

This is me teaching body pump!

his is me reading a bedtime story to Ciara and her brother James.

On safari after chemo with the Venters – Esna and Brennie showing me the ropes.

Acknowledgements

So, two years on, what has changed? Well, my diet is much healthier and I wouldn't go back to eating dairy. But more importantly, after living through cancer, I feel that I have been given a second chance and I have ensured I use every moment.

I have qualified as a fitness instructor. Probably the oldest fitness instructor in the world, but I love it! I teach body pump which is my absolute passion. I have become very interested in health and diet and have taken my nutrition exams. I have also qualified as a business coach and written this book!

I am now working part time for the Royal College of Paediatrics and Child Health and loving every minute of it. So, make the most of your second chance.

THANK YOU

Thank you to Mr Vashisht, my breast cancer surgeon who did everything he could and more. He was absolutely brilliant. To Dr Charles Lowdell my oncologist who was so caring and would always find time to listen and help. To the staff at the Churchill Clementine Hospital, especially Mr B who would change his shifts to ensure he was on duty when I was being operated on, just to make sure I was okay. And all the team at the Oncology unit at Parkside, who made the chemo bearable and helped me cope with losing my hair, and gave me hope.

For my family and friends – thank you for being there for me. I have never been very good at accepting help. Far too stubborn and independent. But everyone was just brilliant.

A SPECIAL THANKS TO:

Every 3 weeks for 24 weeks I had chemo and on the Monday evening following chemo I would stay with Helen and Dave and their two children, James and Ciara, for the night. I remember James who was then 4¾ went to school one day and said very matter of factly: Our friend Lois is staying with us and she has got cancer and wears a hat!

And thank you to Sue, my closest friend, who lost her mum through cancer and every time she saw me was reminded of what her mum had gone through – so it was also a very difficult time for her.

To Mandy and Sally who took me to hospital and made sure I was okay. To Brendan and Anneme, who looked after me when it was all over. To Liz and Tony who took me for walks by the seaside and didn't mind when I fell asleep over dinner! And of course, my mum and dad, big brother and big sis. Finally, Isobel and Joy who made this book possible. Thank you.

HOW CAN YOU HELP?

Please get your friends to buy the book so we can ensure that we support research into breast cancer and help fight this disease.

Healthy eating following cancer   87

Supper party menus

Here are a few suggestions for how you can mix and match the recipes in this book to have a great meal with friends.

SPRING MENU

- Melon and avocado salad   30
- Pasta with bacon, prawns and rocket   40
- Orange slices and Cointreau   79

SUMMER MENU

- A selection of dips: hummus, guacomole, smoked trout pâté with warm crusty bread or pitta bread   24
- Warm spinach, bacon and cherry tomato salad   33
- Strawberries dipped in chocolate   78

WINTER MENU

- Butternut squash soup   14
- Tray baked salmon with olives, green beans, anchovies and tomatoes   50
- Almond torte   82